NOEL GALLAGHERS HIGH FLYING BIRDS

CHASING YESTERDAY

WISE PUBLICATIONS
part of The Music Sales Group
London / New York / Paris / Sydney / Copenhagen /
Berlin / Madrid / Hong Kong / Tokyo

Published by
Wise Publications
14-15 Berners Street, London W1T 3LJ, UK.

Exclusive Distributors:
Music Sales Limited
Distribution Centre, Newmarket Road,
Bury St Edmunds, Suffolk IP33 3YB, UK.
Music Sales Pty Limited
4th floor, Lisgar House, 30-32 Carrington Street,
Sydney, NSW 2000, Australia.

Order No. AM1010889
ISBN: 978-1-78558-012-3
This book © Copyright 2015 Wise Publications,
a division of Music Sales Limited.

Edited by Adrian Hopkins.
Music arranged by Matt Cowe.
Music processed by Paul Ewers Music Design.

Printed in the EU.

Your Guarantee of Quality:

As publishers, we strive to produce every book
to the highest commercial standards.

This book has been carefully designed to minimise awkward
page turns and to make playing from it a real pleasure.

Particular care has been given to specifying acid-free, neutral-sized paper
made from pulps which have not been elemental chlorine bleached.
This pulp is from farmed sustainable forests and was produced
with special regard for the environment.

Throughout, the printing and binding have been planned to ensure a sturdy,
attractive publication which should give years of enjoyment.

If your copy fails to meet our high standards,
please inform us and we will gladly replace it.

www.musicsales.com

RIVERMAN

Words & Music by Noel Gallagher

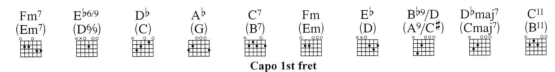

Capo 1st fret

Intro

♩ = 86

N.C.

Spoken: One, two three, four.

Gtr. 1 (acous. steel str.)
Capo 1st fret

mf

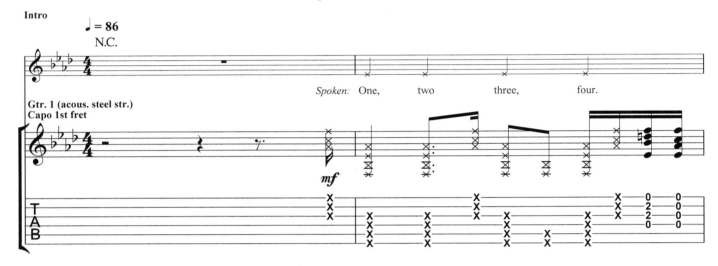

*Symbols in parentheses represent chord names with respect to capoed guitar. (Tab 0 = 1st fret)
Symbols above represent actual sounding chords

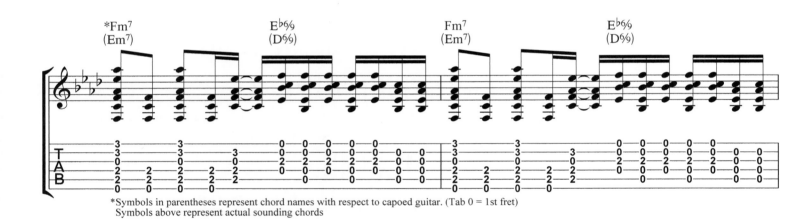

Whispered: Chi -

cont. in slashes

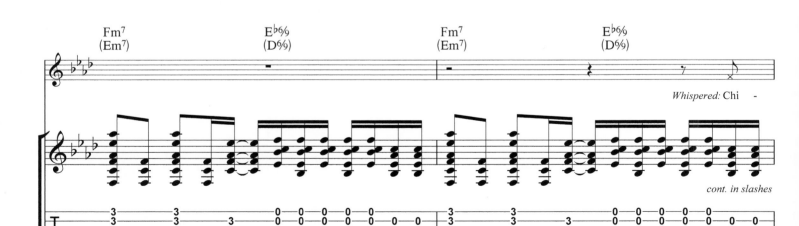

Fm (Em) E♭ (D) D♭ (C) A♭ (G)

___ be - hind ___ is gone. ___ But the Ri-ver-man ___ runs, ___

C⁷ (B⁷) Fm (Em) E♭ (D) *To Coda* ✛ B♭9/D (A⁹/C♯)

find me the girl ___ who e - lec - tri - fied ___ the storm, ___ 'cause in a

D♭maj⁷ (Cmaj⁷) C¹¹ (B¹¹) Fm⁷ (Em⁷) E♭6/9 (D6/9)

lit - tle while ___ she'll ___ be gone. ___

(1°) **Gtr. 3 (elec.) Capo 1st fret**

w/dist.   Gtr. 2 plays Fig. 1 *(x2)*

Fm⁷ (Em⁷) E♭6/9 (D6/9) Fm⁷ (Em⁷) E♭6/9 (D6/9)

Yay, ___ yay, ___ yeah.

9

IN THE HEAT OF THE MOMENT

Words & Music by Noel Gallagher

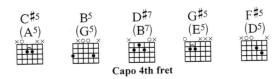

*Symbols in parentheses represent chord names with respect to capoed guitar. (Tab 0 = 4th fret)
Symbols above represent actual sounding chords

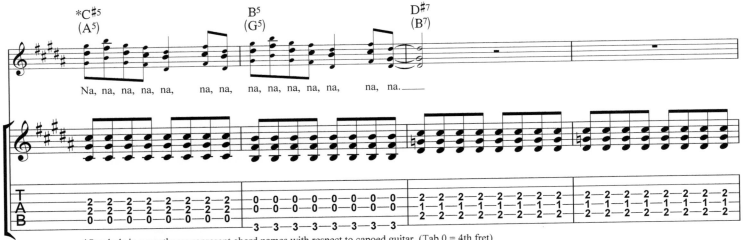

14

15

THE GIRL WITH X-RAY EYES

Words & Music by Noel Gallagher

she's gon-na see through my dis - guise.

Verse

2. Go-ing no - where down a hill___ is hard to swal-low like the pill
(%) 3. Turn the page___ and let it go___ like your mo - ther told you so.

(%) (2°) Gtr. 2

(%) (2°) Gtr. 3

cont. ad lib. sim.

that was twist - ed on___ your tongue___ by the sea___ that was stand - ing
Life it stretch - es out___ for miles,___ the truth is on your ste - re - o.

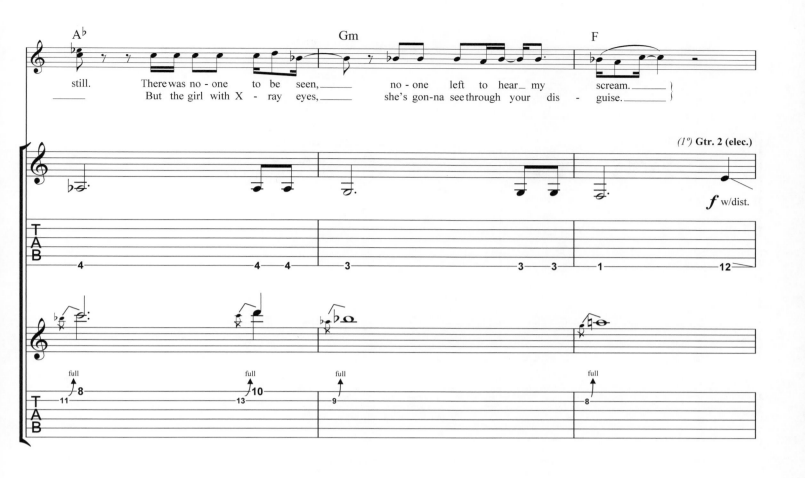

still.

There was no - one to be seen,_____ no - one left to hear__ my scream._____

But the girl with X - ray eyes,_____ she's gon-na see through your dis - guise._____

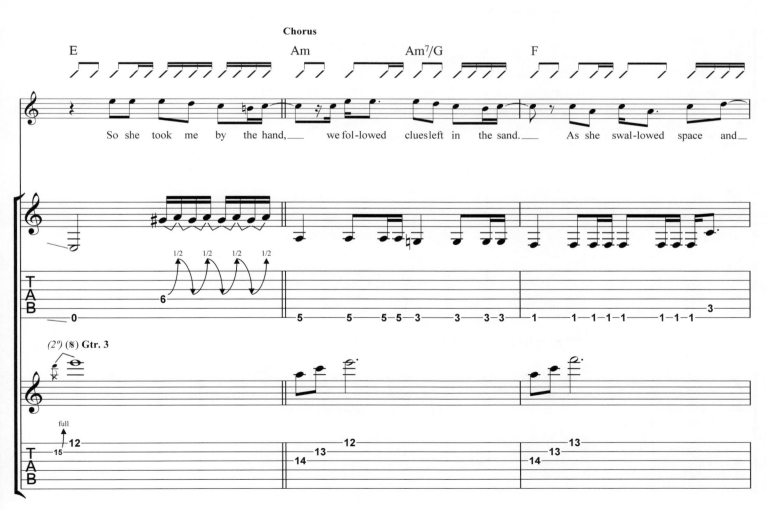

Chorus

So she took me by the hand,____ we fol-lowed clues left in the sand.____ As she swal-lowed space and__

time we ga-thered pearls and swine. She shot me to the sun like a bul-let from a gun.

And when the deed was done in the morn - ing she was gone.

Mellotron arr. for Gtr.

To Coda

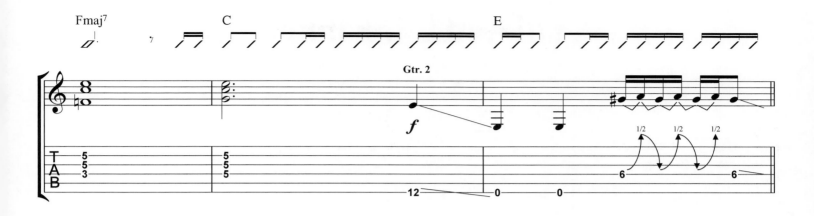

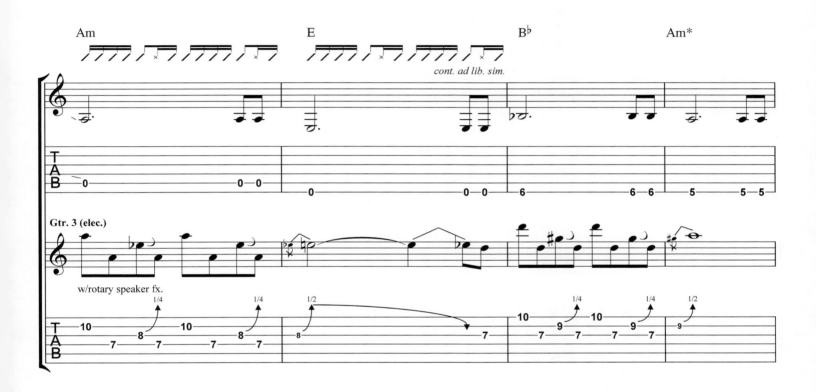

D.S. al Coda   ⊕ **Coda**

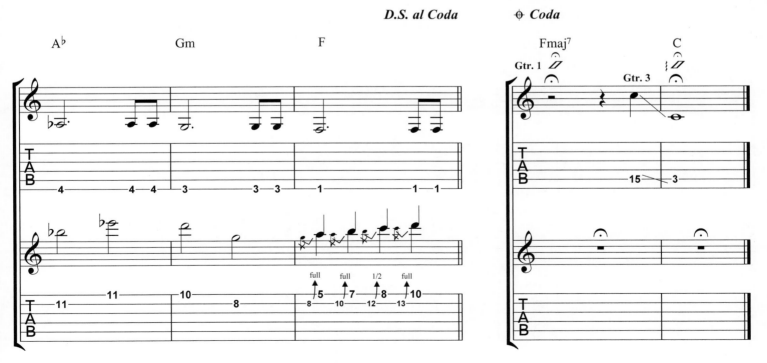

21

LOCK ALL THE DOORS

Words & Music by Noel Gallagher

*Symbols in parentheses represent chord names with respect to capoed guitar. (Tab 0 = 5th fret)
Symbols above represent actual sounding chords

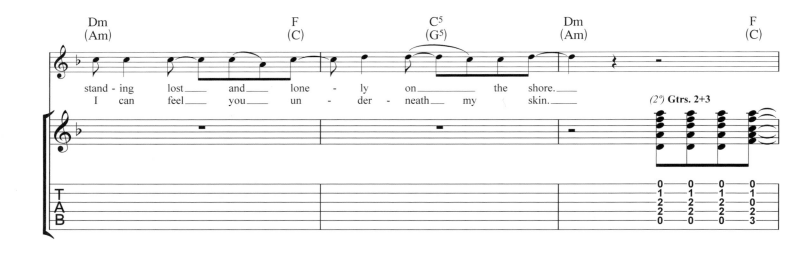

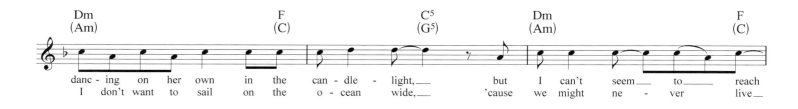

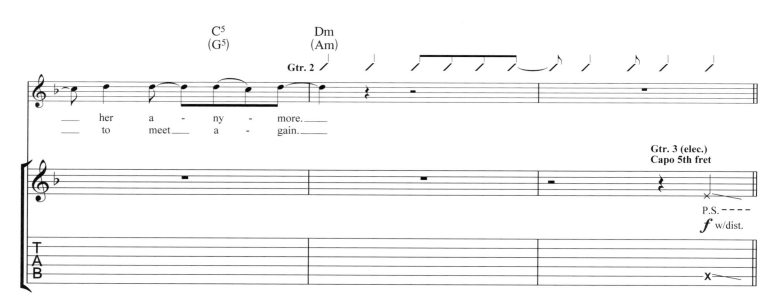

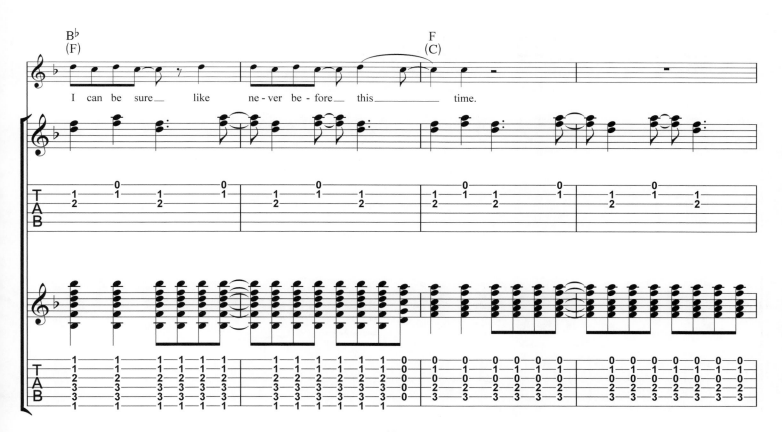

25

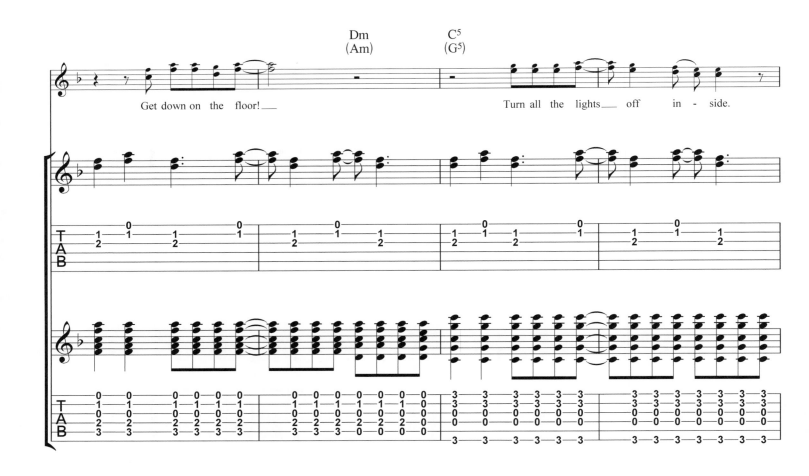

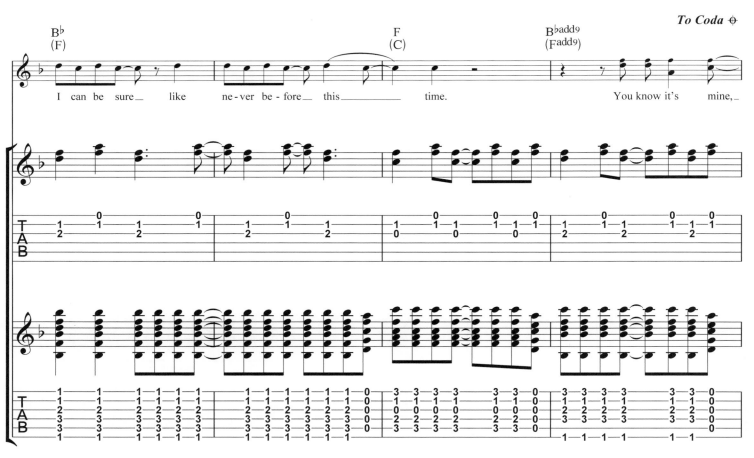

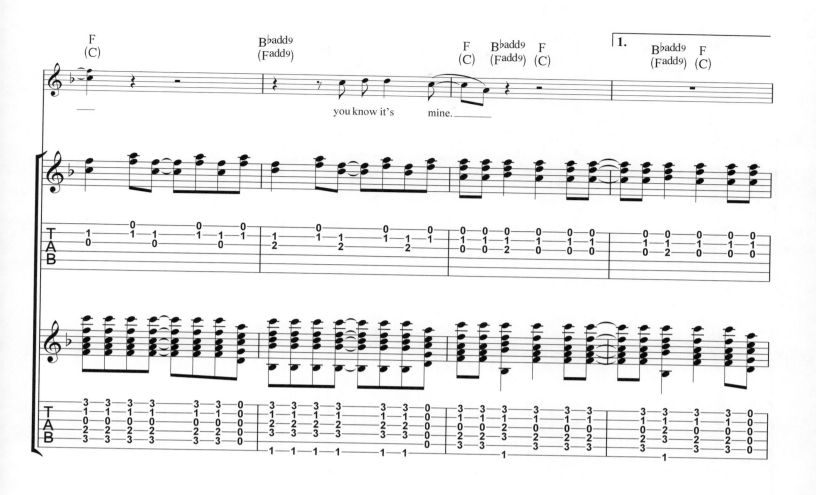

you know it's   mine.

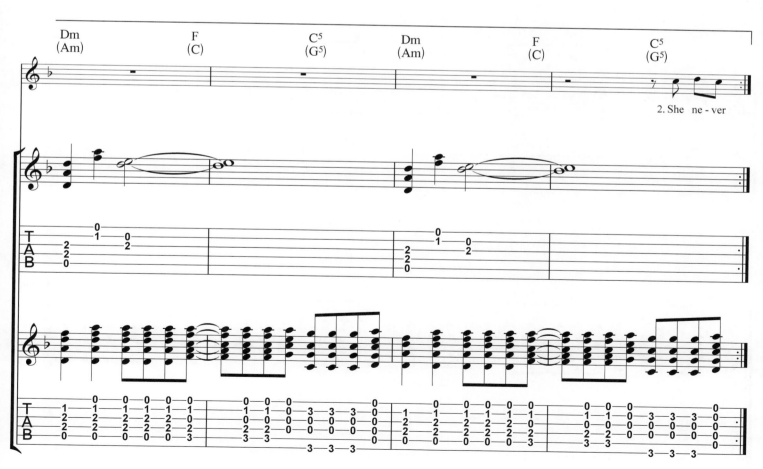

2. She ne - ver

27

you know it's mine,___   you know it's mine.

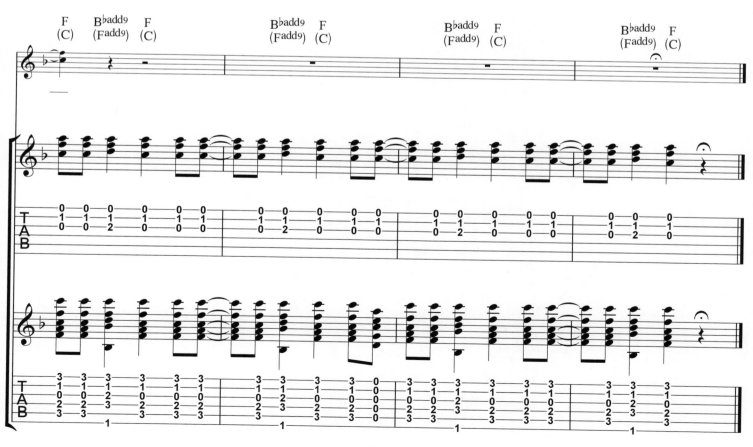

THE DYING OF THE LIGHT

Words & Music by Noel Gallagher

*Symbols in parentheses represent chord names
with respect to capoed guitar. (Tab 0 = 3rd fret)
Symbols above represent actual sounding chords

1. I keep on run-ning but I can't get to the moun - tain, be-the
2. Woke up sleep-ing on a train that was bound for no - where, the

31

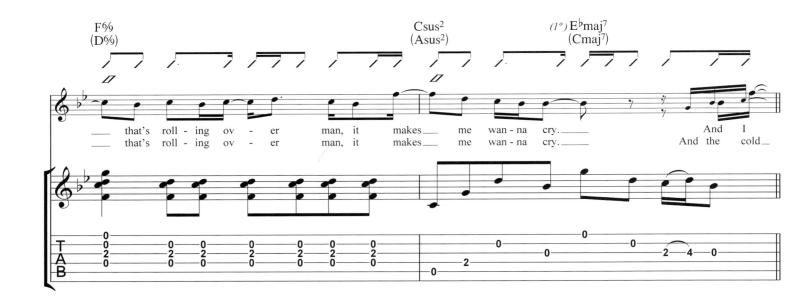

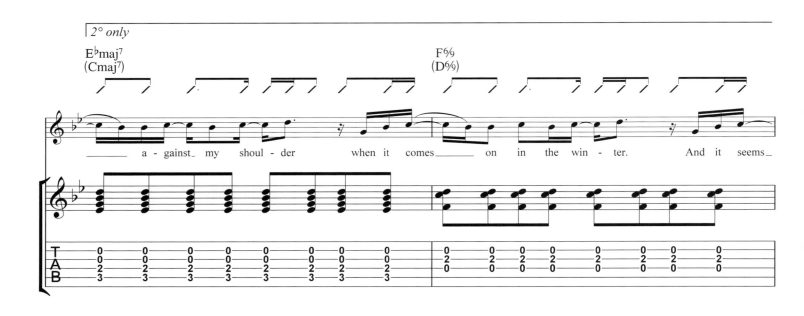

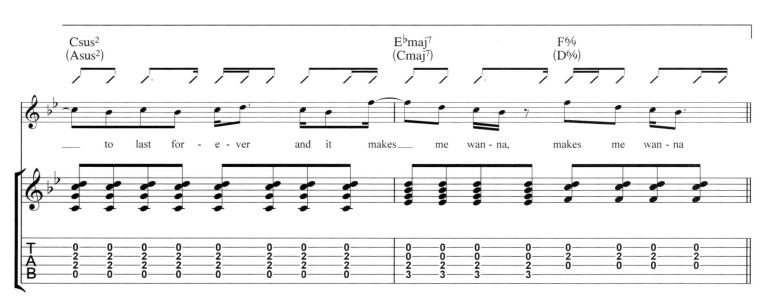

34

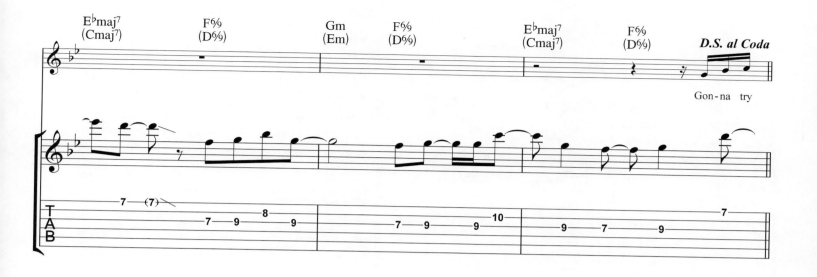

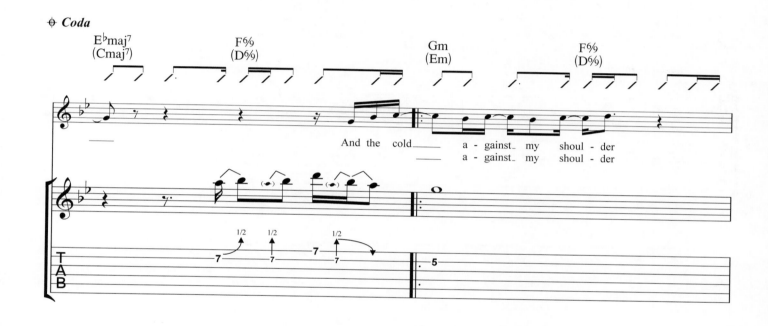

YOU KNOW WE CAN'T GO BACK

Words & Music by Noel Gallagher

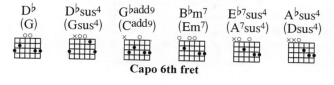

Capo 6th fret

*Symbols in parentheses represent chord names with respect to capoed guitar. (Tab 0 = 6th fret) Symbols above represent actual sounding chords

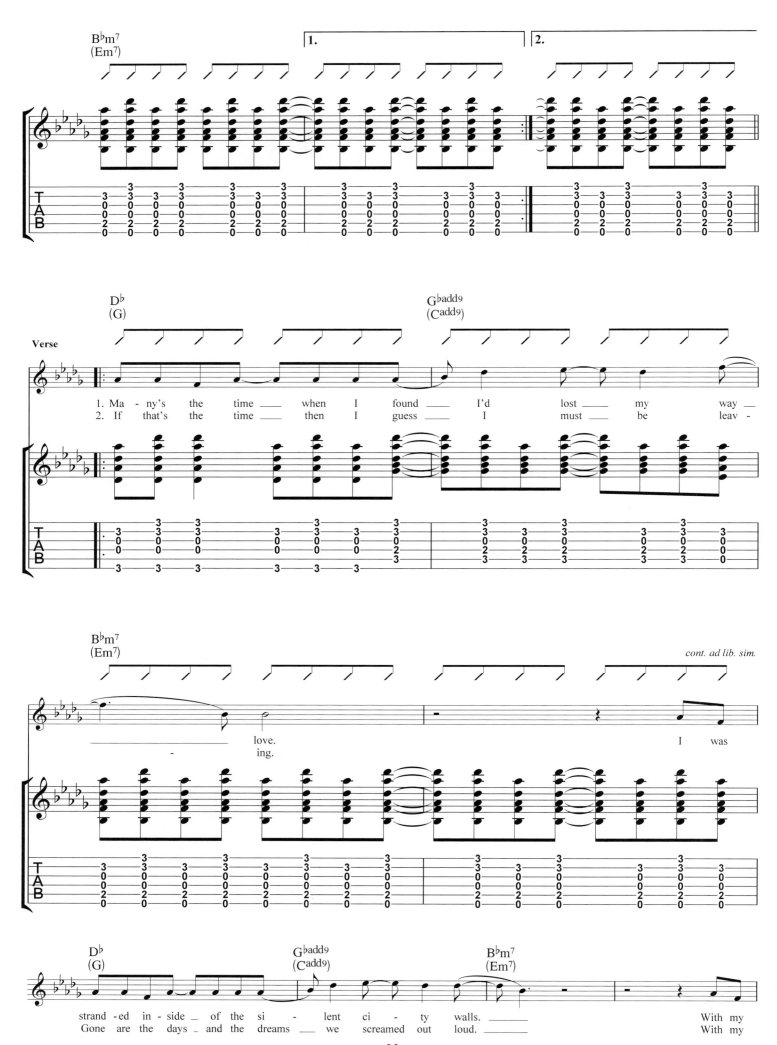

38

39

And it's al -

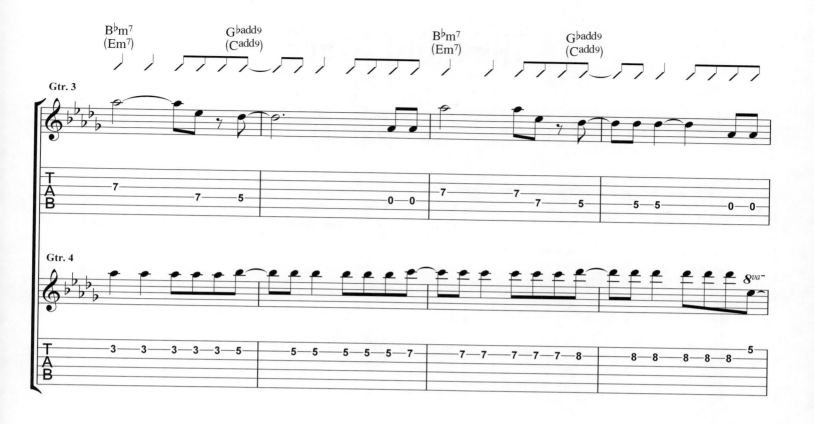

We can't go ___ back. ___

THE RIGHT STUFF

Words & Music by Noel Gallagher

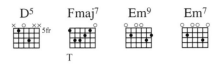

To match original recording tune all guitars down one whole tone

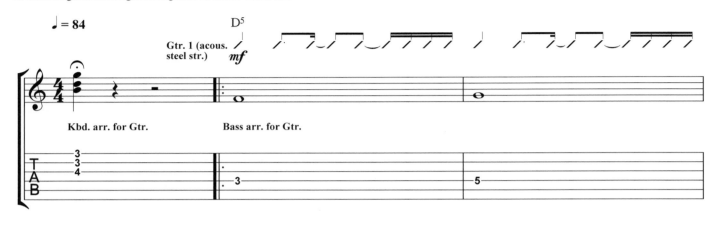

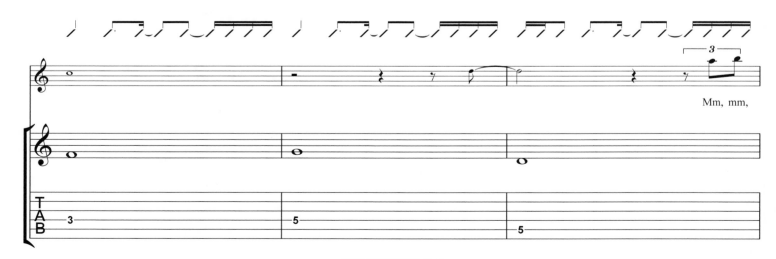

45

"Give me your soul and I'll be on my way..."
Are you the de - vil with a heart of gold?

You and I

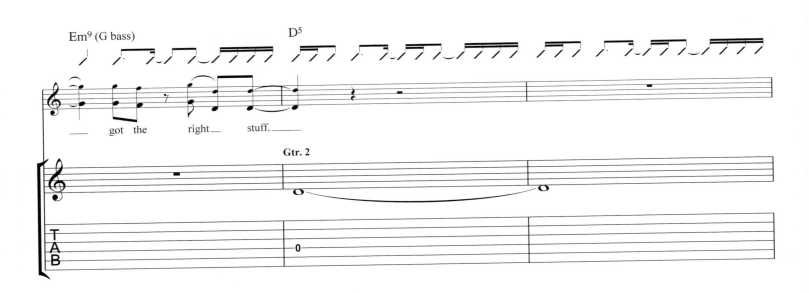

got the right stuff.

Gtr. 2

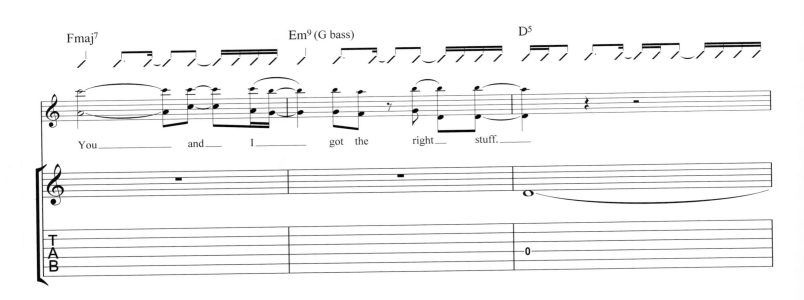

You and I got the right stuff.

Kbd. Brass arr. for Gtr.

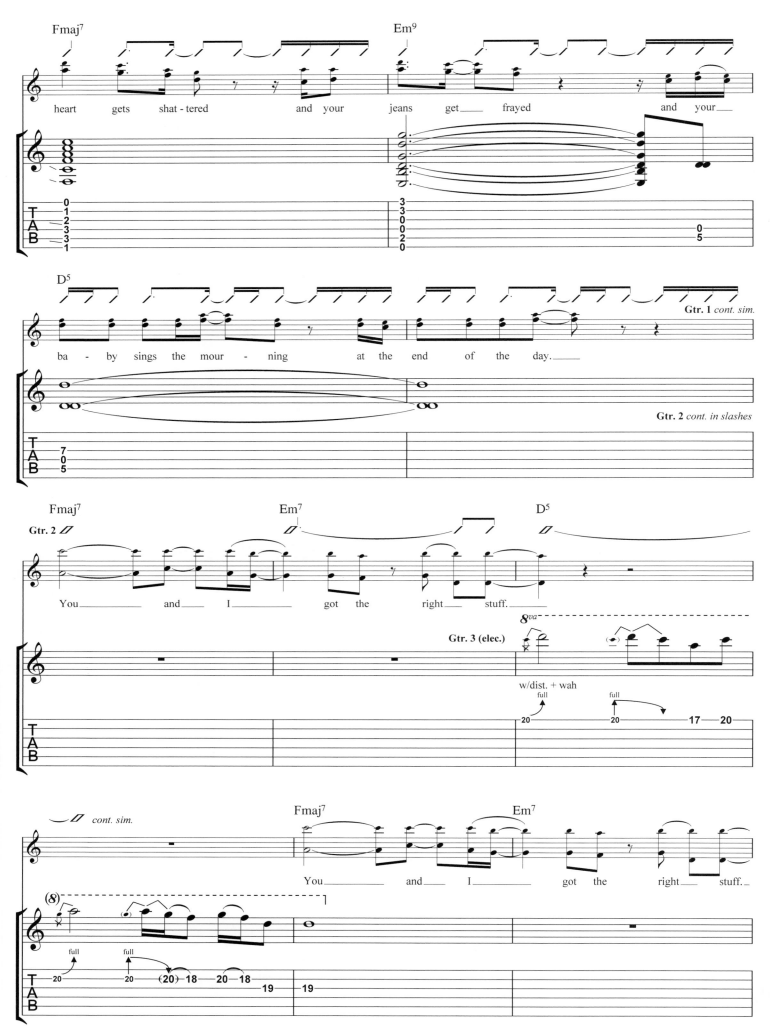

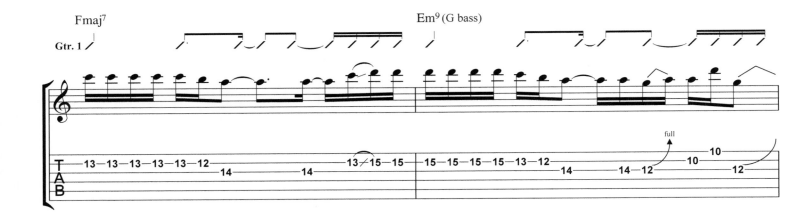

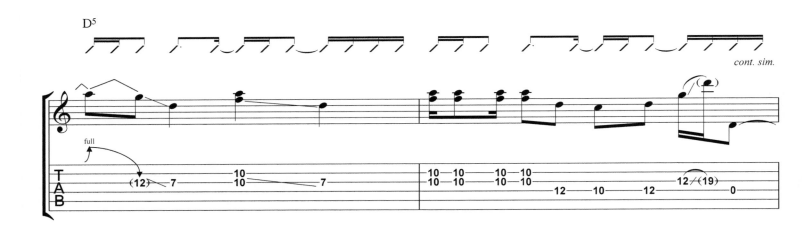

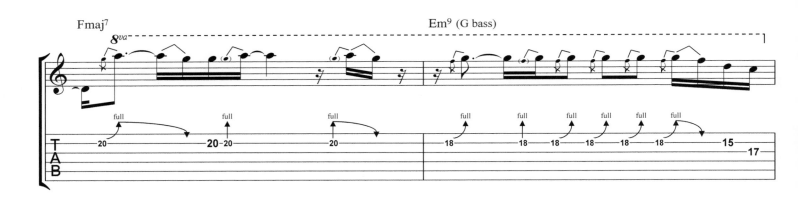

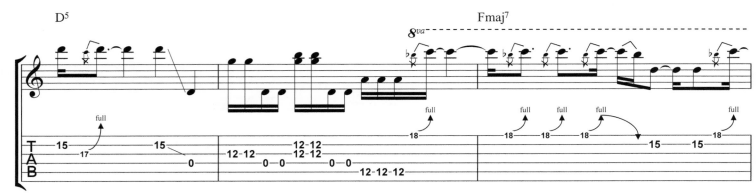

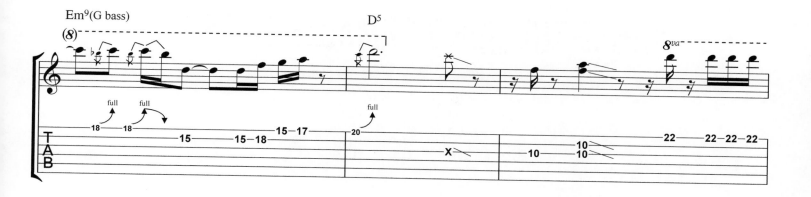

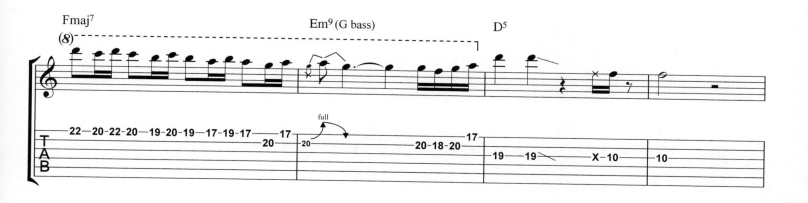

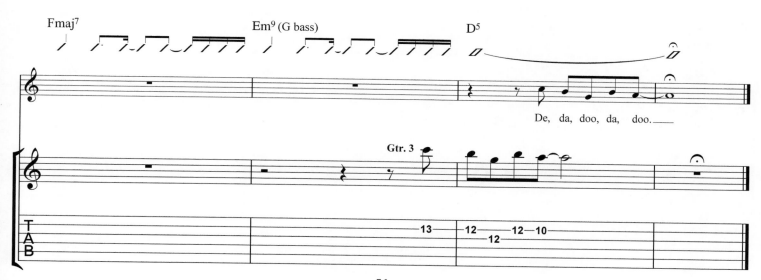

De, da, doo, da, doo.____

WHILE THE SONG REMAINS THE SAME

Words & Music by Noel Gallagher

*Symbols in parentheses represent chord names with respect to capoed guitar. (Tab 0 = 3rd fret)
Symbols above represent actual sounding chords

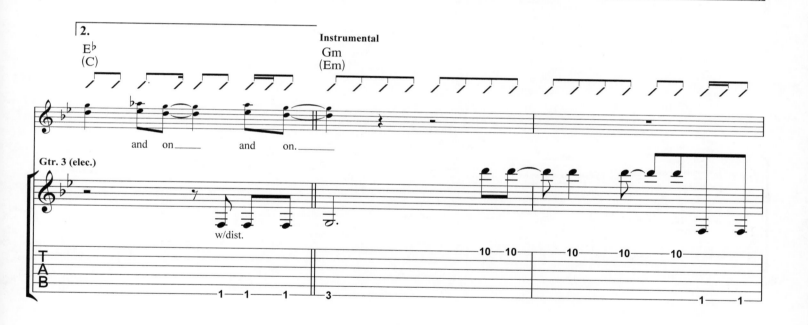

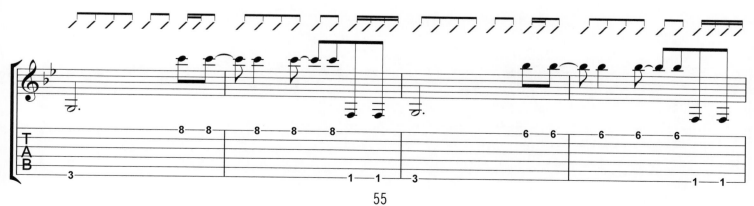

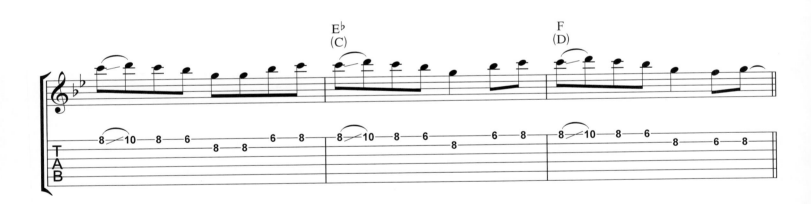

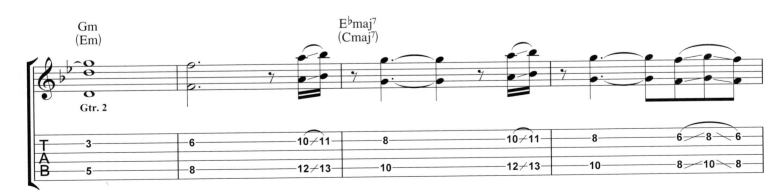

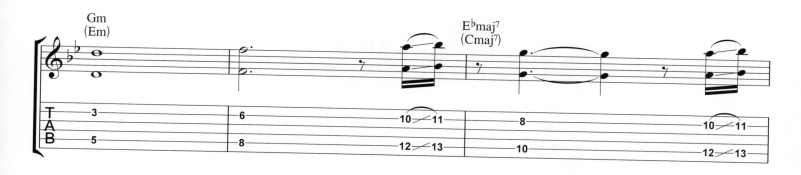

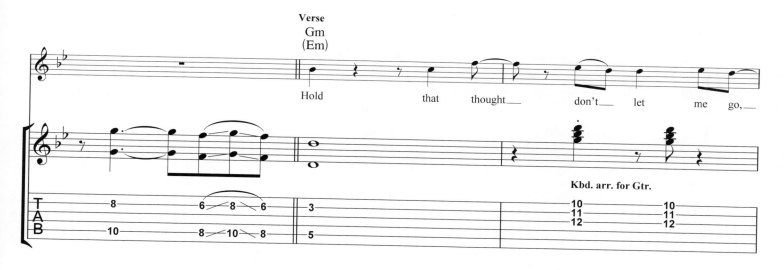

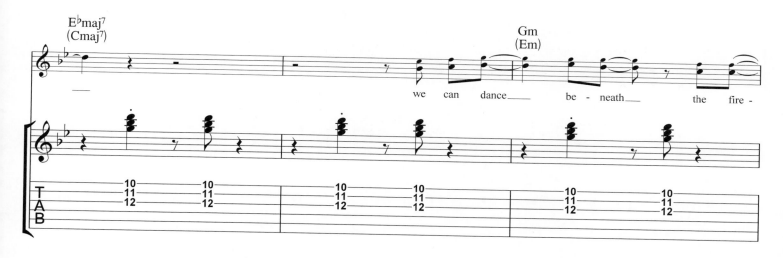

THE MEXICAN

Words & Music by Noel Gallagher

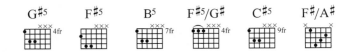

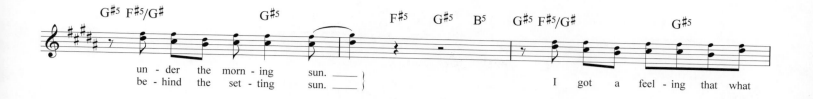

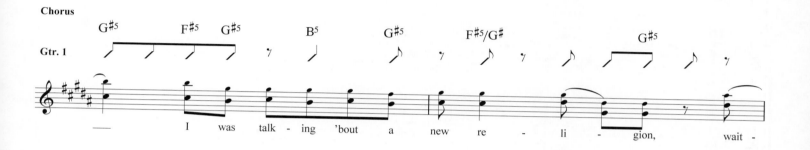

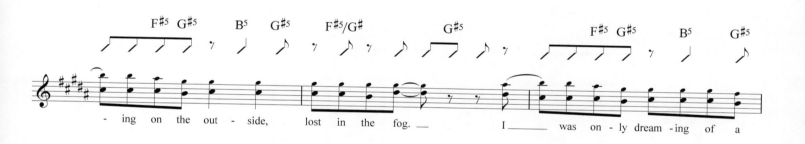

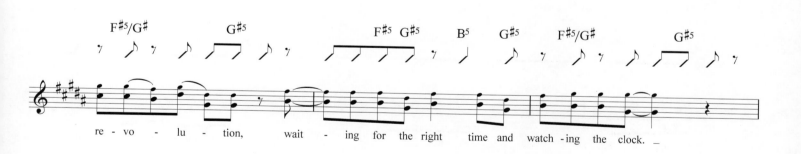

Wah, wah, wah, wah, wah, wah, wah, wah, wah, wah, wah, wah, wah, wah, wah, wah, wah, wah, wah, wah.

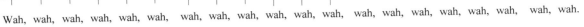

D.S. al Coda

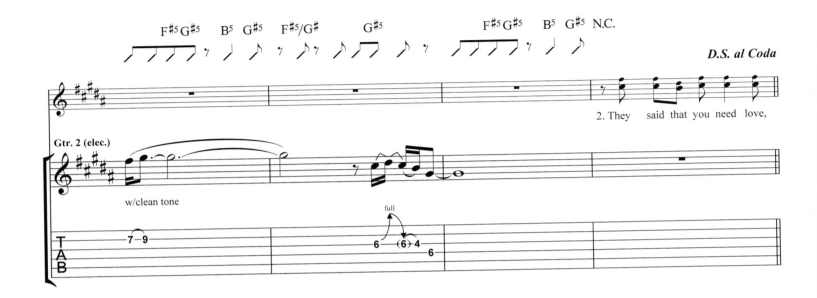

Gtr. 2 (elec.)

w/clean tone

2. They said that you need love,

full

Coda

Chorus

f

Thought — I was talk-ing 'bout a new re-li-gion, wait-

-ing on the out-side, lost in the fog. — I____ was on-ly dream-ing of a

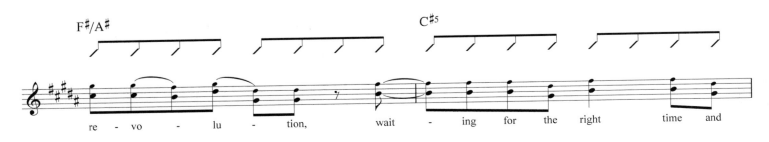

re-vo-lu-tion, wait-ing for the right time and

watch - ing   the   clock.

Instrumental

1.

2.

Thought

61

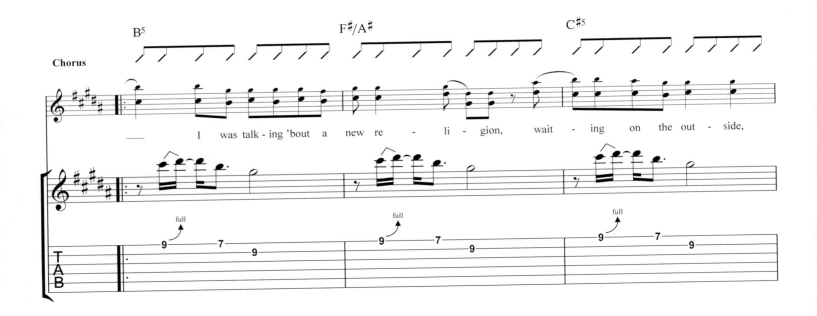

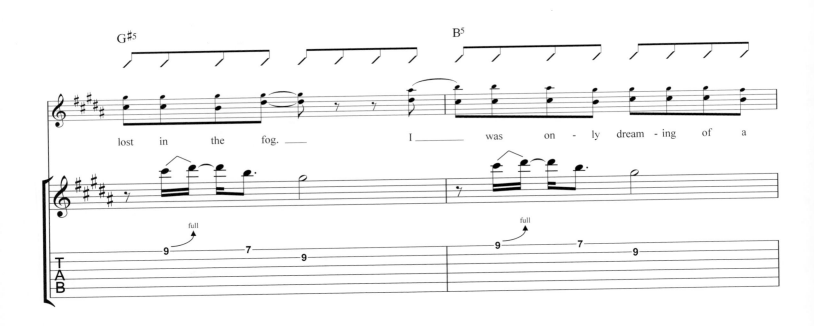

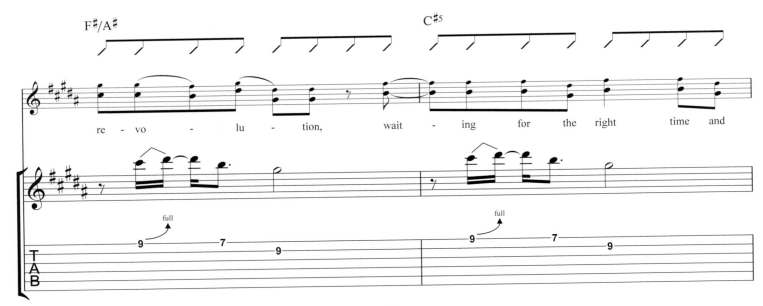

BALLAD OF THE MIGHTY I

Words & Music by Noel Gallagher

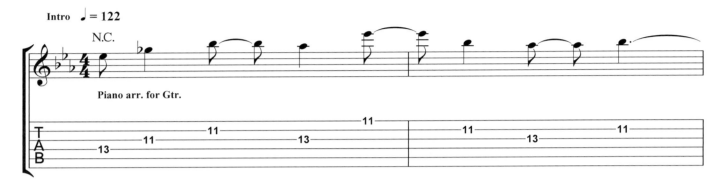

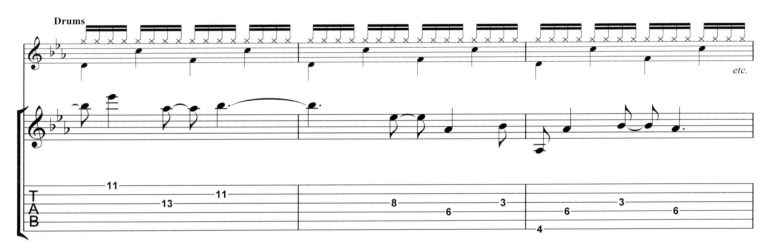

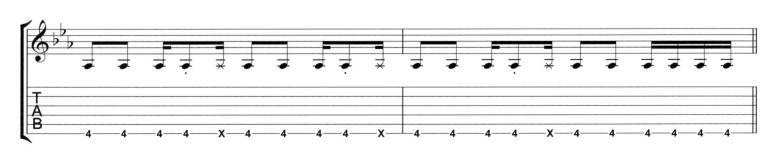

67

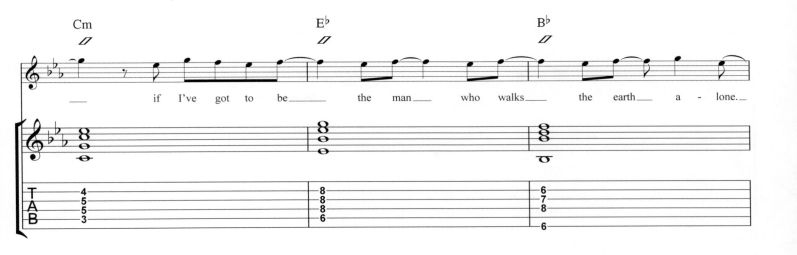

if I've got to be the man who walks the earth a - lone.

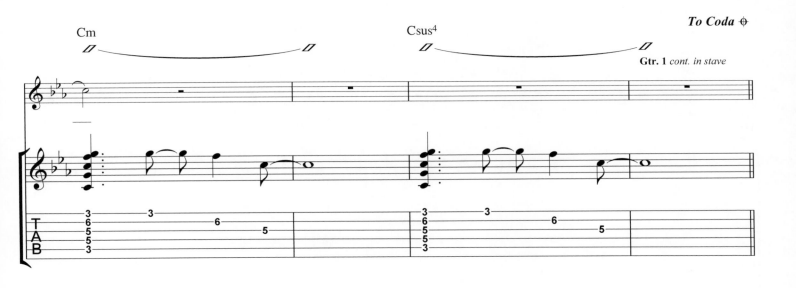

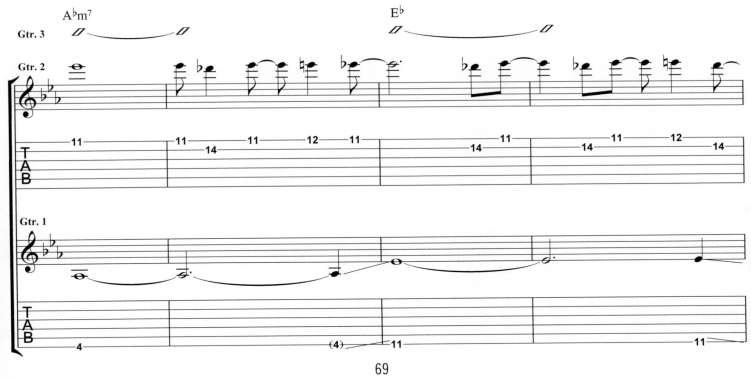

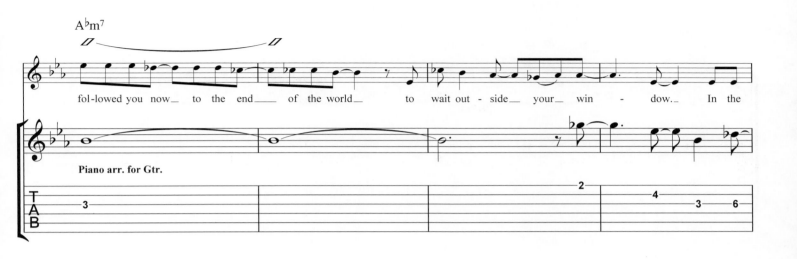

fol-lowed you now_ to the end__ of the world__ to wait out-side__ your__ win - dow._ In the

Piano arr. for Gtr.

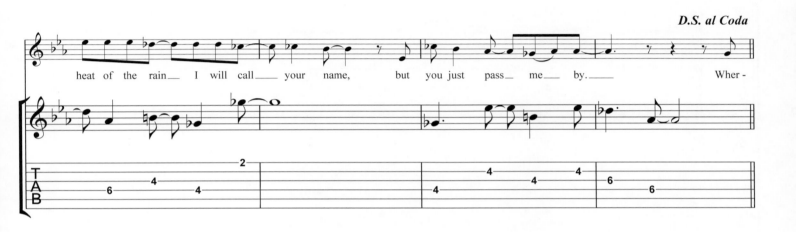

D.S. al Coda

heat of the rain__ I will call__ your name, but you just pass__ me__ by.____ Wher -

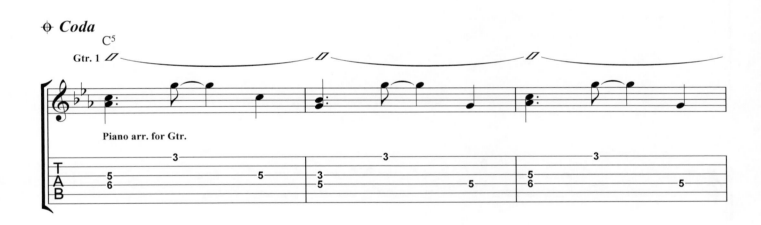

Coda

Gtr. 1

Piano arr. for Gtr.

cont. ad lib. sim.

71

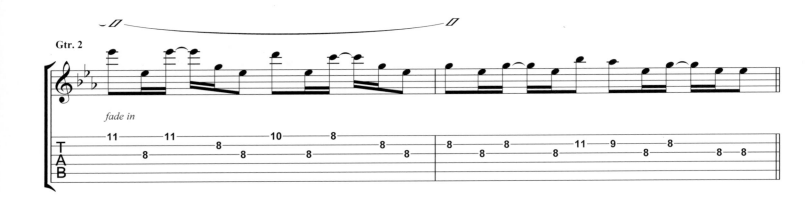

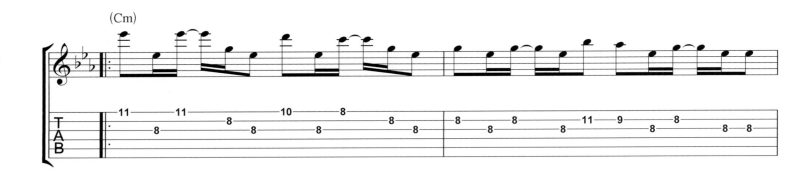

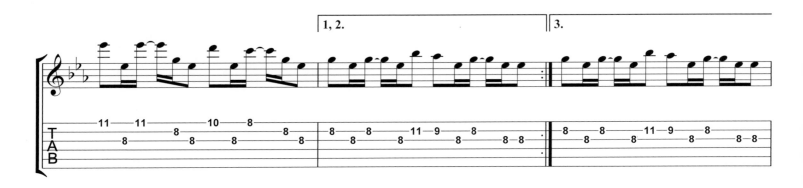

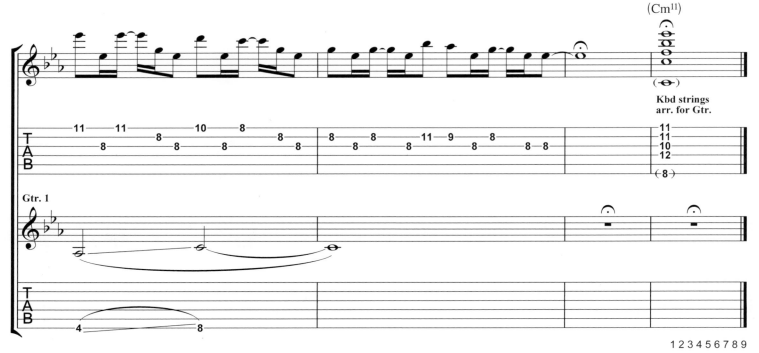

123456789